ONE MORE TIME
SONGS FOR PARTIES, PUBS & CLUBS

First Published 1985
© International Music Publications Limited
Southend Road, Woodford Green,
Essex IG8 8HN, England

Medley 1

ROLL OUT THE BARREL
(BEER BARREL POLKA)

Words by Lew Brown,
Music by Jaromir Vejvoda,
Title and idea by W.A. Timm

Roll out the bar-rel, _____ We'll have a bar-rel of fun. _____ Roll out the bar-rel, _____ We've got the blues on the run. _____ Zing! Boom! ta-ra-rel, _____ Ring out a song of good cheer. _____ Now's the time to roll the bar-rel _____ for the gang's all here. here. _____

THE MORE WE ARE TOGETHER

Words and Music by Irving King

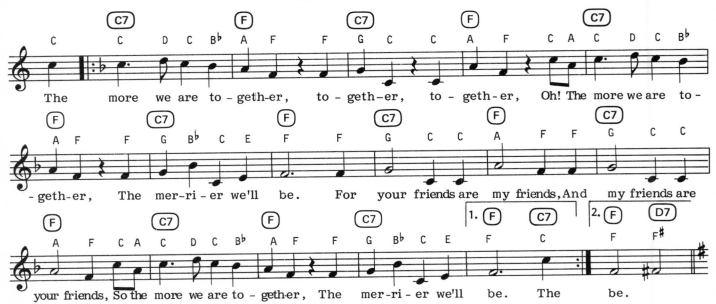

The more we are to-geth-er, to-geth-er, to-geth-er, Oh! The more we are to-geth-er, The mer-ri-er we'll be. For your friends are my friends, And my friends are your friends, So the more we are to-geth-er, The mer-ri-er we'll be. The be.

ANY OLD IRON

By Charles Collins
E.A. Sheppard & Fred Terry

An-y old iron, a - ny old iron, A-ny a-ny a-ny old i - ron?

You look neat, talk a-bout a treat, You look dap-per from your nap-per to your feet,

Dress'd in style, brand new tile, And your fath-er's old green tie on, But I

would-n't give you tup-pence for your old watch chain, Old i - ron, old i - ron? i - ron?

DON'T DILLY DALLY ON THE WAY

By Charles Collins & Fred W. Leigh

My old man said "Fol-low the van, Don't dil-ly dal-ly on the

way!" Off went the cart with the home packed in it, I walked be-

-hind with my old cock lin-net. But I dil-lied and dal-lied, dal-lied and dil-lied,

Lost the van and don't know where to roam. ___ You can't trust the 'spe-cials' like the old time

'cop-pers' When you can't find your way home. home. ___

ANOTHER LITTLE DRINK WOULDN'T DO US ANY HARM

Words by Clifford Grey
Music by Nat D. Ayer

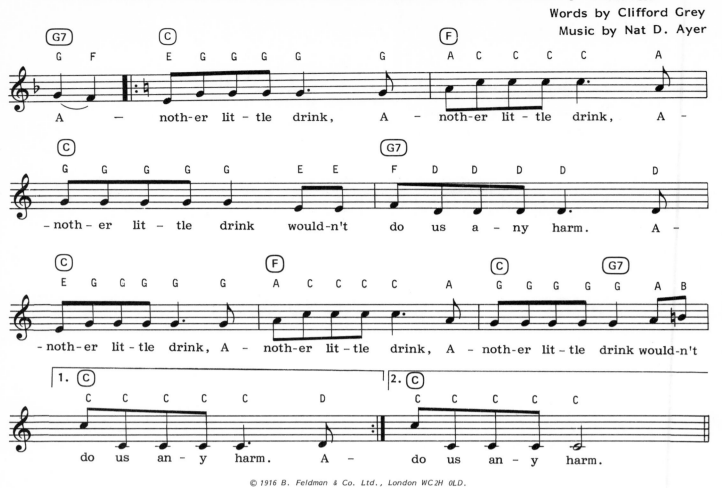

TAVERN IN THE TOWN

Traditional

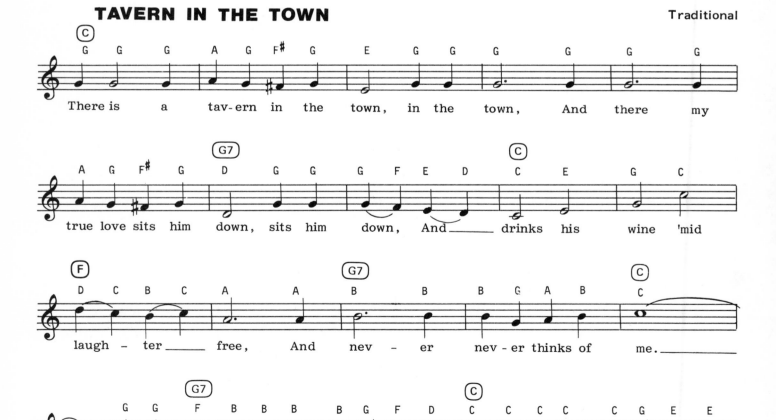

WHERE DID YOU GET THAT HAT?

By J. Rolmaz

Medley 2

HERE WE ARE AGAIN

By Fred Godfrey & Billy Williams

LET'S ALL GO DOWN THE STRAND

By Harry Castling & C.W. Murphy

WOT CHER!
(KNOCKED 'EM IN THE OLD KENT ROAD)

Words by Albert Chevalier
Music by Charles Ingle

"Wot cher!" all the neigh-bours cried, "Who're yer goin' to meet Bill?

Have yer bought the street Bill?" Laugh! I thought I should 'ave died,

Knock'd 'em in the Old Kent Road! Road!

WAITING AT THE CHURCH

By Henry Pether & Fred W. Leigh

I'VE GOT A LOVELY BUNCH OF COCOANUTS

By Elton Box, Desmond Cox and Lewis Ilda

Medley 3

Words by Billy Rose,
Music by Al Jolson & Dave Dreyer

ME AND MY SHADOW

MOONLIGHT BAY

Words by E. Madden
Music by P. Wenrich

© Redwood Music Ltd., London W1X 2LR.

BY THE LIGHT OF THE SILVERY MOON

Words by E. Madden
Music by G. Edwards

© Redwood Music Ltd., London W1X 2LR.

HELLO DOLLY!

Words and Music by Jerry Herman

Medley 4

SWEET ROSIE O'GRADY/HOW CAN YOU BUY KILLARNEY?
THE ROSE OF TRALEE/THE WILD ROVER
WHEN IRISH EYES ARE SMILING

SWEET ROSIE O'GRADY

By Maude Nugent

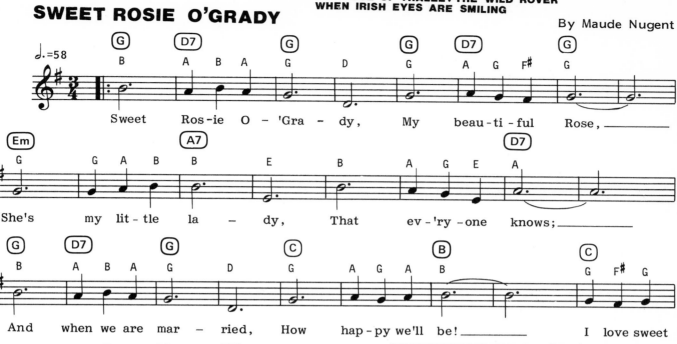

Sweet Ros-ie O -'Gra-dy, My beau-ti-ful Rose, _____

She's my lit-tle la -dy, That ev-'ry -one knows; _____

And when we are mar—ried, How hap-py we'll be! _____ I love sweet

Ros-ie O -'Gra -dy, And Ros-ie O -'Gra-dy loves me. _____ me.

HOW CAN YOU BUY KILLARNEY?

By Hamilton Kennedy, Freddie Grant,
Gerald Morrison & Ted Steels

How can you buy all the stars in the skies? How can you buy two

blue I-rish eyes? How can you pur-chase a fond mo-ther's sighs? How can you

buy Kil -lar —ney? Na—ture be-stowed all her gifts with a

smile, The em-'rald, the shamrock, the blar —ney. When you can buy all these

won-der-ful things, Then you can buy Kil-lar —ney. -ney.

THE ROSE OF TRALEE

Words by C. Mordaunt Spencer
Music by Charles W. Glover

This arrangement © 1985 International Music Publications, Ilford, Essex IG1 2AQ.

THE WILD ROVER

Traditional

This arrangement © 1985 International Music Publications, Ilford, Essex IG1 2AQ.

WHEN IRISH EYES ARE SMILING

Words by Chauncey Olcott & George Graff Jr.,
Music by Ernest R. Ball

Medley 5

**HONEYSUCKLE AND THE BEE/DADDY WOULDN'T BUY ME A BOW-WOW
STROLLIN'/FOR ME AND MY GIRL/ON MOTHER KELLY'S DOORSTEP**

HONEYSUCKLE AND THE BEE

Words by Albert H. Fitz
Music by William H. Penn

© 1901 Sol Bloom (USA)
sub-published by Francis Day & Hunter Ltd., London WC2H 0LD.

DADDY WOULDN'T BUY ME A BOW-WOW

By Joe Tabrar

This arrangement © 1985 International Music Publications, Ilford Essex IG1 2AQ.

STROLLIN'

By Ralph Reader

Words by Edgar Leslie
Music by George W. Meyer

FOR ME AND MY GIRL

ON MOTHER KELLY'S DOORSTEP

By George Stevens

Medley 6

TWO LOVELY BLACK EYES

By Charles Coborn

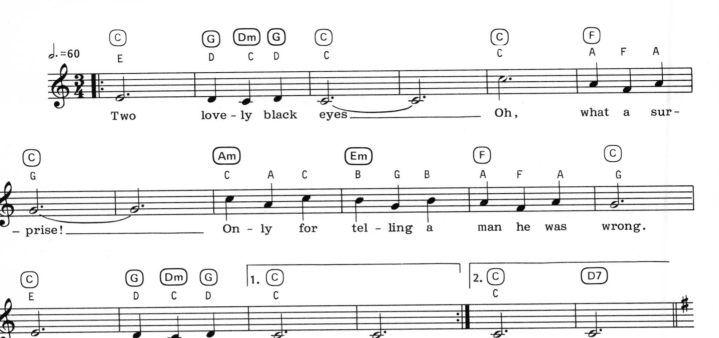

COMRADES

By Felix McGlennon

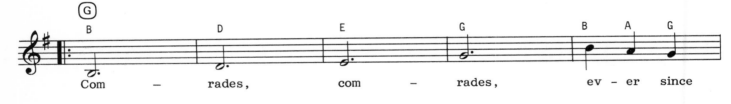

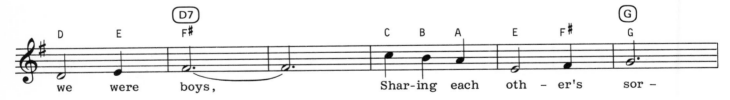

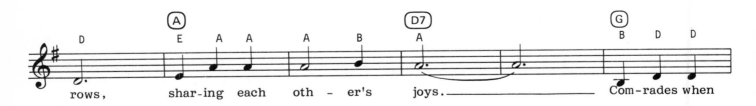

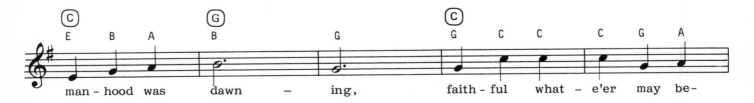

JOSHUAH

By George Arthurs & Bert Lee

I BELONG TO GLASGOW

By Will Fyffe

AFTER THE BALL

By Charles K. Harris

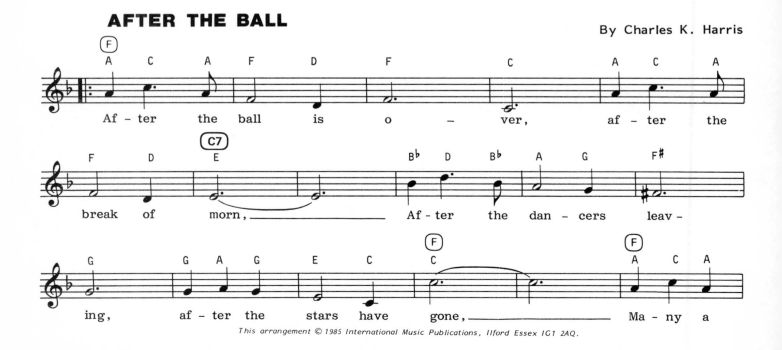

This arrangement © 1985 International Music Publications, Ilford Essex IG1 2AQ.

DOWN AT THE OLD BULL AND BUSH

Music by Harry Von Tilzer,
Words by Percy Krone,
Andrew B. Sterling & Russell Hunting

Medley 7

APRIL SHOWERS

Words by B.G. De Sylva
Music by Louis Silvers

SONNY BOY

By B.G. De Sylva, Lew Brown
Ray Henderson & Al Jolson

HEART OF MY HEART

Words by J. Arther Lamb
Music by Albert Von Tilzer

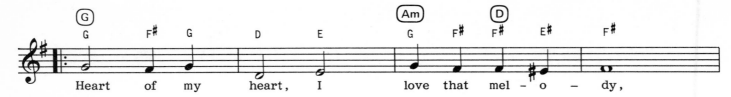

Heart of my heart, I love that mel - o - dy,

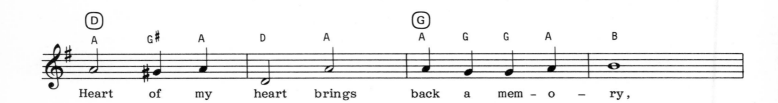

Heart of my heart brings back a mem - o - ry,

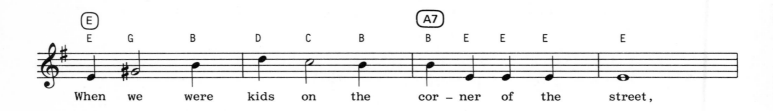

When we were kids on the cor - ner of the street,

We were rough and read - y guys, But Oh! how we could har - mon - ize.

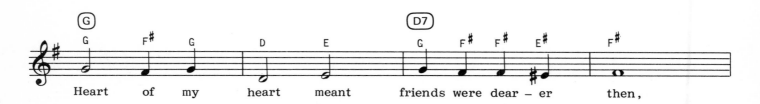

Heart of my heart meant friends were dear - er then,

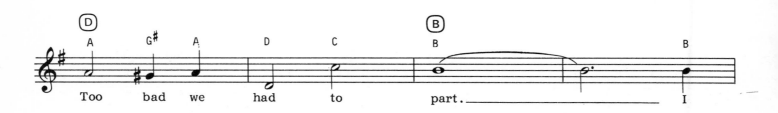

Too bad we had to part._____ I

know a tear would glis - ten, if once more I could

I SEE THE MOON

By Meredith Willson

Medley 8

I LOVE A LASSIE

By Harry Lauder & G. Grafton

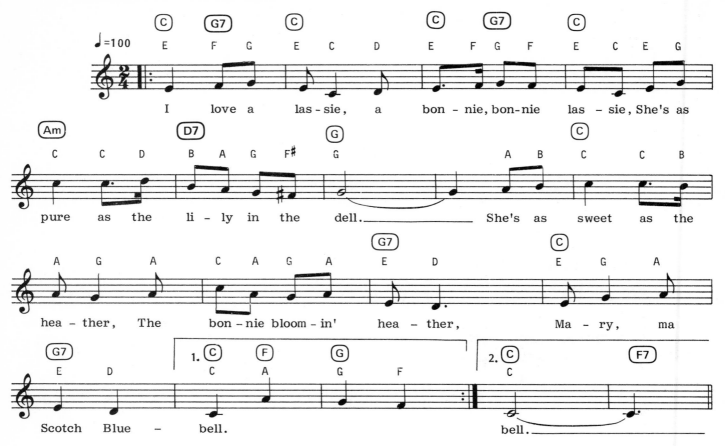

I love a las-sie, a bon-nie, bon-nie las-sie, She's as pure as the li-ly in the dell. She's as sweet as the hea-ther, The bon-nie bloom-in' hea-ther, Ma-ry, ma

1. Scotch Blue-bell.
2. bell.

JUST A WEE DEOCH - AN - DORIS

Music by Whit Cunliffe,
Words by R.F. Morrison

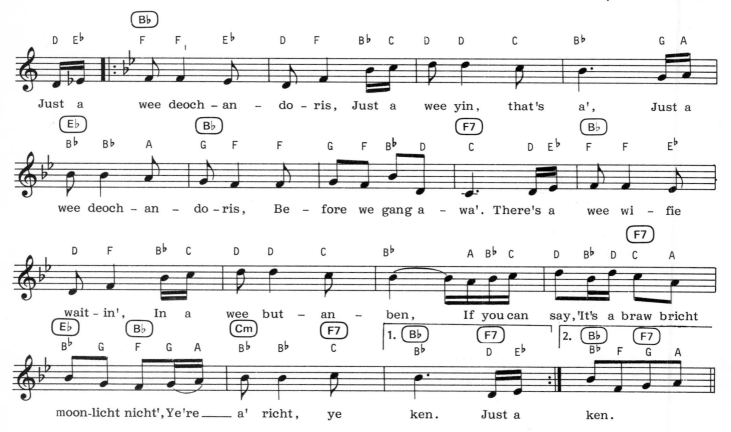

Just a wee deoch-an-do-ris, Just a wee yin, that's a', Just a wee deoch-an-do-ris, Be-fore we gang a-wa'. There's a wee wi-fie wait-in', In a wee but-an-ben, If you can say, 'It's a braw bricht moon-licht nicht', Ye're ___ a' richt, ye ken. Just a ___ ken.

THE END OF THE ROAD

Words and Music by
William Dillon and Harry Lauder

Medley 9

OH JOHNNY! OH JOHNNY! OH!

By Ed Rose and Abe Olman

SWANEE

Music by George Gershwin
Words by I. Caesar

I'M JUST WILD ABOUT HARRY

By Noble Sissle & Eubie Blake

WHEN THE SAINTS GO MARCHING IN

Traditional

Medley 10

IN THE SHADE OF THE OLD APPLE TREE

By Egbert Van Alstyne
& Harry Williams

MEMORIES

Words by Gus Kahn
Music by Egbert Van Alstyne

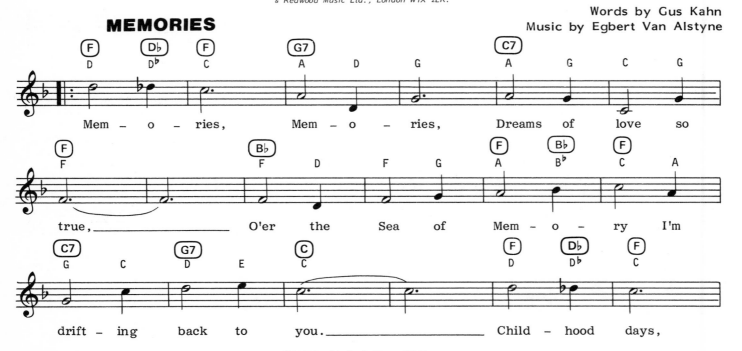

I'M FOREVER BLOWING BUBBLES

By Jaan Kenbrovin
& John William Kellette

Medley 11

MEN OF HARLECH

Traditional

Men of Har - lech, wake from sleep-ing, Sax -on tyr-ants now are creep-ing,

Like a riv - er on-ward sweep-ing, Swift - ly through the night.

Fight for wives and moth-ers, Chil - dren sis - ters broth-ers, Your

coun - try needs your gal - lant deeds, To save your-selves and oth - ers.

Whilst the bat - tle drums are beat - ing, This your war-cry, this your greet - ing,

"No sur-ren - der, no re-treat-ing! Har-lech wins the fight!" fight!"

This arrangement © 1985 International Music Publications, Ilford, Essex IG1 2AQ.

SOSPAN FACH

Traditional

My sweet Mar - y Ann's hurt her lit - tle fin - ger And Dav - id the ser-vant is-n't

2. sweet Mar - y Ann her___ fin - ger's bet - ter And Dav - id the ser-vant he is

This arrangement © 1985 International Music Publications, Ilford, Essex IG1 2AQ.

WE'LL KEEP A WELCOME

Words and Music by Mai Jones
Lyn Joshua and James Harper

Medley 12

DELILAH

By Les Reed & Barry Mason

IF I HAD MY LIFE TO LIVE OVER

Words and Music by Henry Tobias
Moe Jaffe and Larry Vincent

AROUND THE WORLD

Words by Harold Adamson
Music by Victor Young

Medley 13

JOHN BROWN'S BODY

Traditional

THE QUARTERMASTER'S STORE

Traditional

There was beer, beer that makes you feel so queer, in the store, in the store, There was
whiskey, whiskey that makes you feel so frisky, in the store, in the store, There was
tea, tea, but not for you and me, in the store, in the store, There was
booze, booze to chase a-way the blues, in the store, in the store, There was

beer, beer that makes you feel so queer, In the Quar - ter - mas - ter's store.
whiskey, whiskey that makes you feel so frisky, In the Quar - ter - mas - ter's store.
tea, tea, but not for you and me, In the Quar - ter - mas - ter's store.
booze, booze to chase a-way the blues, In the Quar - ter - mas - ter's store.
} Mine

eyes are dim, I can - not see, I have not brought my specs with me, __ I __

have not brought my specs with me. There was me.

This arrangement © 1985 International Music Publications, Ilford, Essex IG1 2AQ.

ROLL ME OVER

By Desmond O'Connor

Now this is num - ber one and my song has just be - gun,
this is num - ber two and I'm get - ting in a stew,
this is num - ber three and he's com - ing up to me,
this is num - ber four, some - one's knock-ing at the door,
this is num - ber five, oh it's good to be a - live,
this is num - ber six and he's up to all his tricks,
this is num - ber seven, this is my i - dea of heaven,
this is num - ber eight, oh I'll have to make him wait,
this is num - ber nine, oh I'll have to go and hide,
this is num - ber ten and he's start - ing once a - gain,
} Roll me

I DO LIKE TO BE BESIDE THE SEASIDE

By John A. Glover-Kind

Medley 14

DEEP IN THE HEART OF TEXAS
YOU ARE MY SUNSHINE
OLD MACDONALD HAD A FARM
SHE'LL BE COMING ROUND THE MOUNTAIN

DEEP IN THE HEART OF TEXAS

By June Hershey & Don Swander

YOU ARE MY SUNSHINE

By Jimmie Davies & Charles Mitchell

OLD MACDONALD HAD A FARM

Traditional

SHE'LL BE COMING ROUND THE MOUNTAIN

Traditional

Medley 15

UNDERNEATH THE ARCHES
YOU MADE ME LOVE YOU
JUST LIKE THE IVY – I'LL CLING TO YOU
WALTZING MATILDA

By Bud Flanagan

UNDERNEATH THE ARCHES

YOU MADE ME LOVE YOU

Words by Joe McCarthy
Music by James V. Monaco

JUST LIKE THE IVY – I'LL CLING TO YOU

By Harry Castling & A.J. Mills

Just like the i-vy on that old gar-den wall,

Cling-ing so tightly, what-e'er may be-fall. As you grow

old-er, I'll be con-stant and true, And just like the

i-vy, I'll cling to you. you.

WALTZING MATILDA

Words and Music by
A.B. Paterson and Marie Cowan

Waltz-ing Ma-til-da, Waltz-ing Ma-til-da, You'll come a-waltz-ing Ma-

-til-da with me, And he sang as he watched and wait-ed till his bil-ly boiled,

'You'll come a-waltz-ing Ma-til-da with me!' -til-da with me!'

Medley 16

LET'S ALL SING LIKE THE BIRDIES SING/DAISY
SHE WAS ONE OF THE EARLY BIRDS/LET ME CALL YOU SWEETHEART
SHE'S A LASSIE FROM LANCASHIRE/I'LL BE YOUR SWEETHEART

LET'S ALL SING LIKE THE BIRDIES SING

Words by Robert Hargreaves & Stanley Damerell
Music by Tolchard Evans

DAISY

By Harry Dacre

SHE WAS ONE OF THE EARLY BIRDS

By T.W. Connor

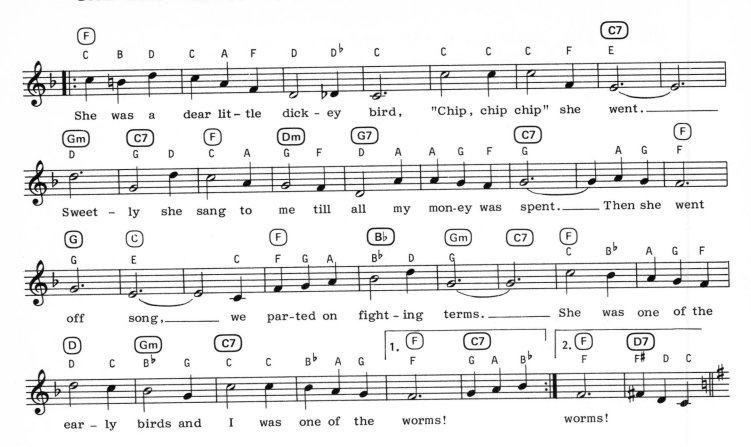

She was a dear lit-tle dick-ey bird, "Chip, chip chip" she went. Sweet-ly she sang to me till all my mon-ey was spent. Then she went off song, we par-ted on fight-ing terms. She was one of the ear-ly birds and I was one of the worms! worms!

© 1895 Francis Day & Hunter Ltd., London WC2H 0LD.

LET ME CALL YOU SWEETHEART

Words by Beth Slater Whitson
Music by Leo Friedman

Let me call you sweet-heart, I'm in love with you. Let me hear you whis-per that you love me too. Keep the love-light glow-ing in your eyes so true. Let me call you sweet-heart, I'm in love with you. you.

SHE'S A LASSIE FROM LANCASHIRE

By C.W. Murphy
Dan Lipton & John Neat

I'LL BE YOUR SWEETHEART

By Harry Dacre

Medley 17

GOODNIGHT SWEETHEART

Words and Music by Ray Noble,
Jimmy Campbell & Reg Connelly

SHOW ME THE WAY TO GO HOME

Words and Music by
Irving King and Hal Swain

WE'LL MEET AGAIN

Words and Music by
Ross Parker & Hughie Charles

Medley 18

THE LAST WALTZ

By Les Reed & Barry Mason

© 1967 Donna Music Ltd., London WC2H 0LD.

WHO'S TAKING YOU HOME TONIGHT?

By Manning Sherwin
& Tommie Connor

© 1939 Francis Day & Hunter Ltd., London WC2H 0LD.

NOW IS THE HOUR

Music by Clement Scott,
Words by Maewa Kaihau

AULD LANG SYNE

Traditional

Printed in Great Britain by Hobbs the Printers Ltd, Totton, Hampshire 11/95